Ben's dragon

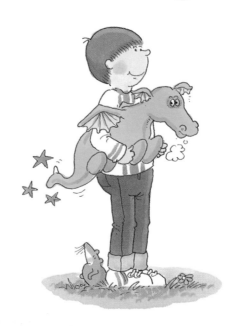

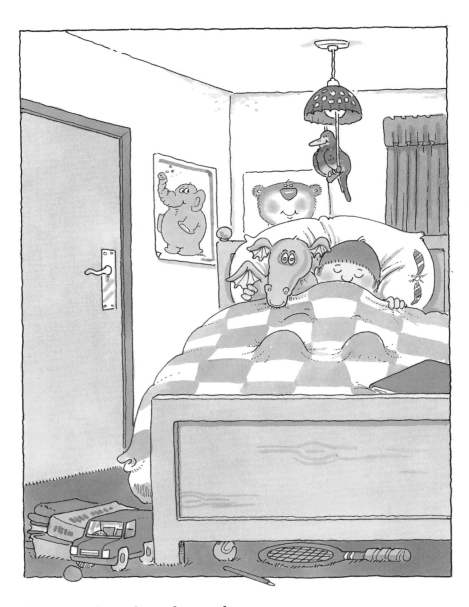

Ben is in bed.

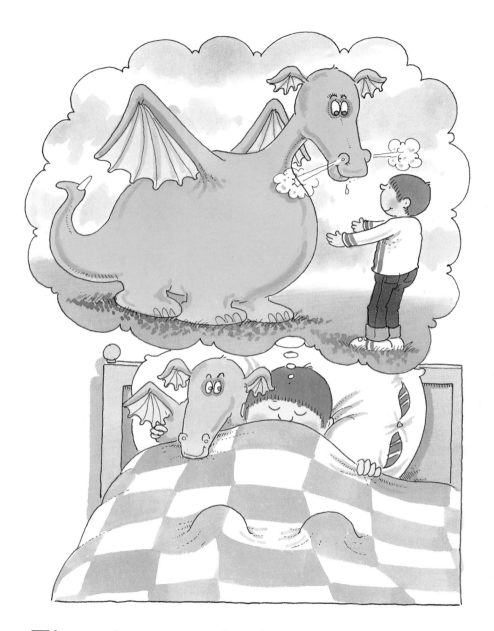

The dragon is in bed.

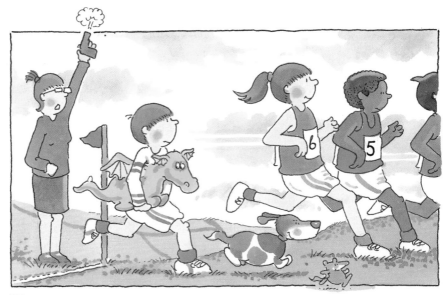

Ben runs.

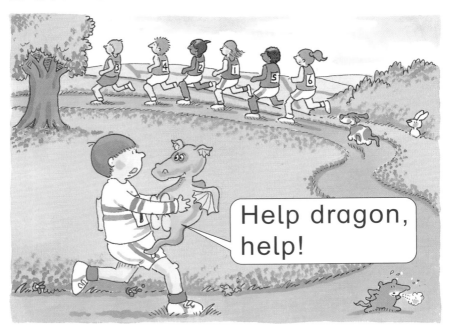

Help dragon, help!

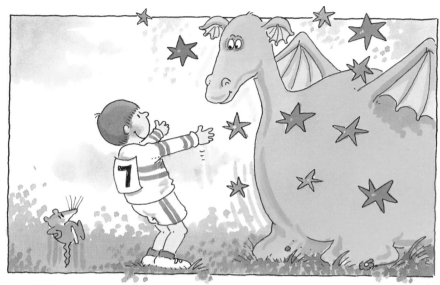

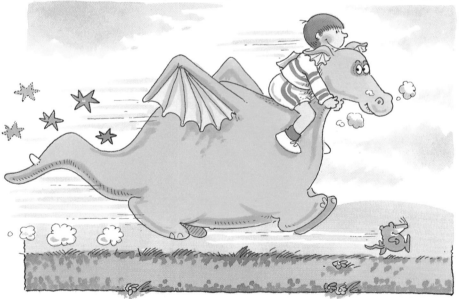

The dragon can run.

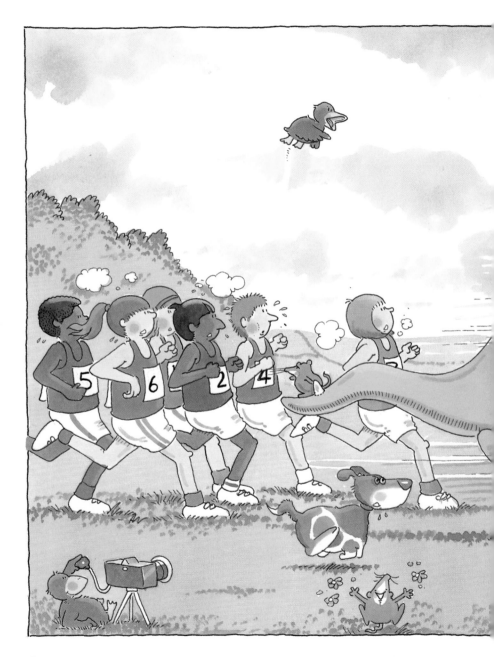

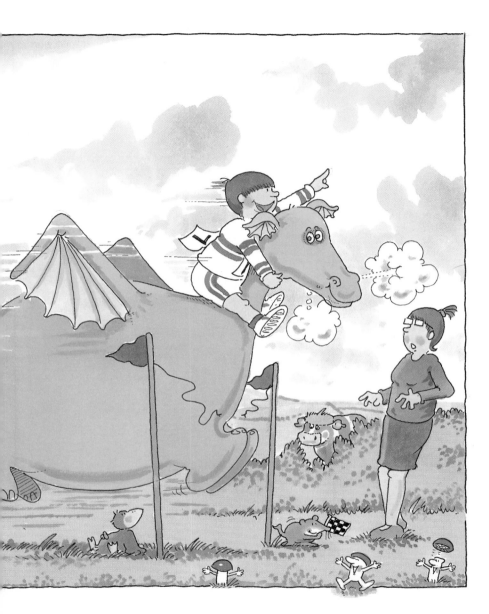

"It is Ben and his dragon!"

Ben swims.

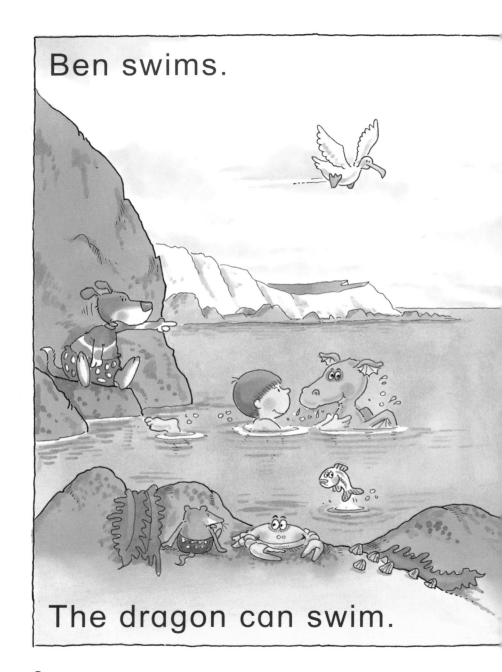

The dragon can swim.

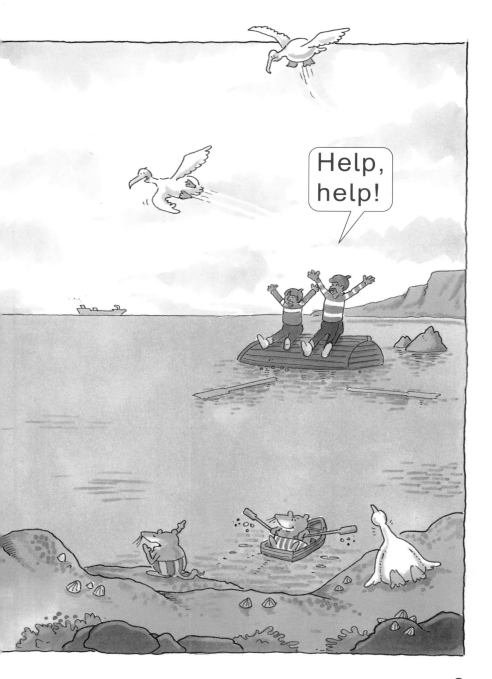

9

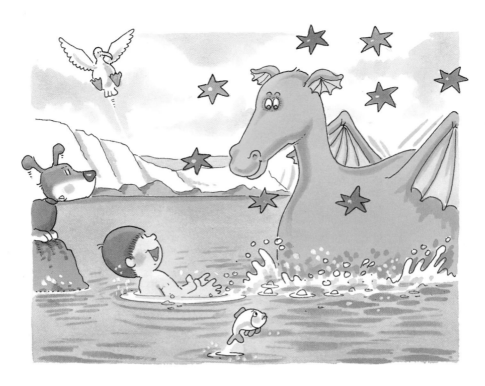

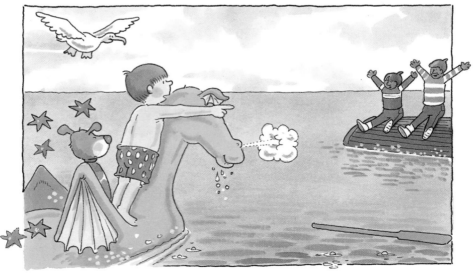

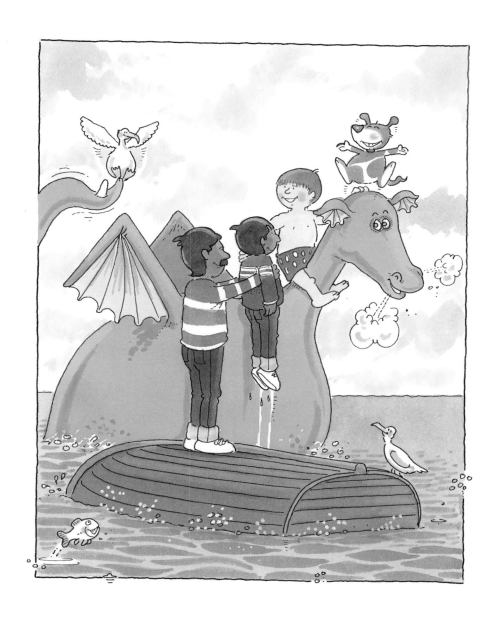

"It is Ben and his dragon!"

Ben helps.

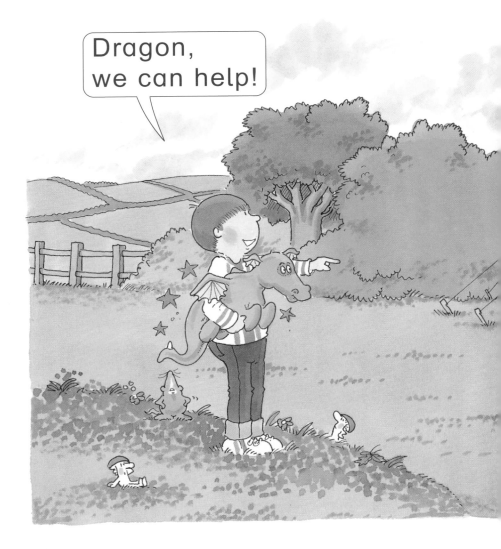

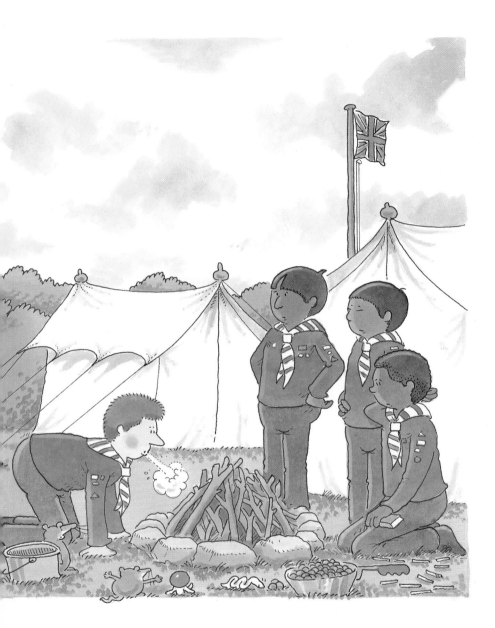

The dragon can help.

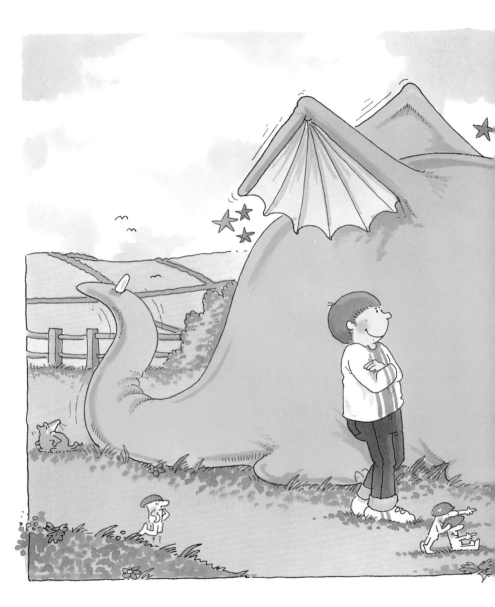

"It is Ben and his dragon!"

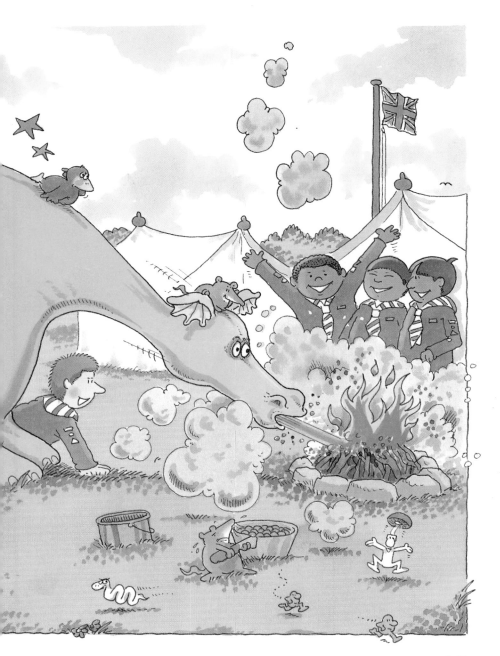

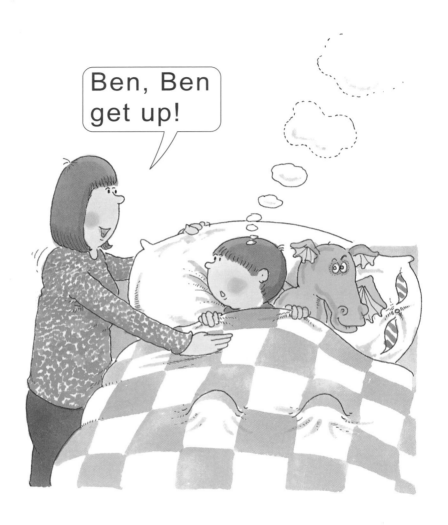